THREE GORGES PROJECT IN CHINA

Chief editor：Lu Jin

The Biggest Key Water Control Project in The World

CHINA FANGZHENG PRESS

Dream is Coming True
(preface)

The Yangtze River, totaling 6,380 kilometers long, is the longest river in China, and the third-longest in the world. The source of the Yangtze River lies to the west of Geladandong Mountain, the principal peak of the Tanggula Mountain chain in the Qinghai-Tibetan Plateau. The river flows from west to east through provinces of Qinghai, Tibet, Sichuan, Yunnan, Chongqing, Hubei, Hunan, Jiangxi, Anhui and Jiangsu as well as the city of Shanghai, finally emptying into the East China Sea. The drainage area of Yangtze River is 1.8 million square kilometer, one fifth of China, where accumulates 40% riches.

The Yangtze River formed 100million years ago, is consider as the cradle of China and the source of ancient civilization, and the Yellow River as well. Along the Yangtze River in the new era, it is full of vital force and energy, flowed with enthusiastic and brilliant years, and stands in the eastern with the colorful charm and boundless vigour. Chinese is completing a grand cross-century work in the Yangtze Three Gorges, which provide the driving energy for the great renewal of the nation in the new century.

On June 1st, 2003, the world famous Yangtze Three Gorges project began to hold water. Ten days later, time brings a great change to the worlds; the whole Yangtze Three Gorges has a crashing change, it become to be a huge artificial lake. On June 16th, the Five-stage Shiplocks began its first test for the navigation. In July, the first group of electricity sets began to work. All of these are the marks for the coming benefits period of Three Gorges Project after the hard ten years.

After the 70-years-dreaming, 50-years-designing and 30-years- argumentation, the dream of Three Gorges comes true. From the first dream about Three Gorges of Sun Zhongshan till now, in the short 86 years, nearly a century, Three Gorges attracted such many attentions of men of the time, arose such heartquake argumentations, and left such many motive stories. There is any task like Three Gorges Project could touch the deep heart of people in the world. The reason is simple, that is the great cost for the project is so heavy, even the greatest in the history. The project change the masterpiece of nature the splendor Three Gorges, the water level in the gorges is rose to 175m, and form a huge reservoir with 39.3 billion m^3 water; what is under the water is the history track of Chinese civilization; it also submerged 2.8 thousand hectare plantation, orchard and woodland, which distributed over 21 countries in Hubei Province and Chongqing Municipality; the whole project will resettled millions of people and cost astronomical financing.

Undoubtedly, we can clearly foresee the hope of the nation brings by Three Gorges Project. We Chinese need Three Gorges Project. In China, the country with frequent floods, we could not defend the wilful flood with our body on the brittle dyke for years; we could not bear the energy flow down vigorously without utilize with the river in the renewal era which starve for the energy; and we also could not slow down the pace of dredging up the golden gullet connected the eastern and western China in the era that empolder the western

China and Yangtze economic zone and even determine the fate the China. That is why the dream comes true with a nearly 100-years gestation. Face to the great change of Yangtze Three Gorges, to record the change correctly with album is the responsibilities of us.

The Three Gorges Project is the dream that make our country stronger, but when the dream comes true, our old but beautiful hometowns also become a parting old dream. It is unavailable to be satisfied for the both sides in the world. Facing the new Three Gorges, there are also coziness and gratification in people's complex sensibility. Losing some beauty of seclusion and grotesque, the Three Gorges increases some magnificence; and the most important is the modern town will dot the reservoir area; the villagers will save more than 50 years to join into the modern life with the construction of the Three Gorges Project. Good wishes for the Three Gorges! Good wishes for the people here! Good wishes for the constructors! No these people, no today's Three Gorges!

Lu Jin
February, 2008

The Great Yangtze Three Gorges Project

Contents

CONTENTS

三峡工程
CHINA
中国 Three Gorges Project

Panorama of the Three Gorges Project

The Great Yangtze Three Gorges Project

Mystery of the Wushan Mountains

The Great Yangtze Three Gorges Project

Flood Discharge of the Three Gorge Project

The Great Yangtze Three Gorges Project

三峡工程
CHINA
中国 Three Gorges Project

A smooth lake rises in the narrow gorges

Five-stage Shiplocks

The Great Yangtze Three Gorges Project

Night Scene of Three Gorges Dam

The Great Yangtze Three Gorges Project

三峡工程
CHINA
中国 Three Gorges Project

The Great Three Gorges Project

The Yangtze Three Gorges Project (TGP) is a strategic project that aims to harness and develop the Yangtze River, and it will benefit mainly in flood control, power generation and navigation improvement. The damsite of TGP is located in Sandouping of Yichang City, 40 miles from Gezhouba Hydropower Plant. After the completion of the project, a river-like reservoir with a storage capacity of 39.3 billion m^2, 21.15 billion m^3 of which will serve as flood control capacity, will be shaped on the upstream of the Yangtze. As a result, the flood preventing capability of Jingjiang river section will be promoted from preventing 10-year flood to preventing 100-year flood. The powerhouses, situated at the toe of the dam, will be equipped with 26 sets of hydro turbine generating units, 700 MW each. With a total installed capacity of 18,200 MW, it will produce an annual average output of 84.7 billion KWh. Hence, it can improve the navigation of 660 km from Yichang to Chongqing, so that 10,000-t ships can directly voyage to Chongqing. Building TGP is a desire to try one's utmost to achieve what one dreams of in several generations in China. Through the last few decades' long-term planning, justification review, decision making, a feasible program was reached. The construction was mobilized in 1993, and on Dec.14, 1994, the commencement was officially announced to the world.

TGP is composed of a dam, a spillway dam, two power plants, a double-way and five-step shiplock, a shiplift, and navigation facilities. It is planned to be completed in three phases with a total construction period of 17 years from 1993 -2009. The duration of phase-one construction is from 1993-1997 whose end is marked by the realization of river enclosure. Phase-two is from 1998-2003 and the major marks are: the preliminary impoundment for the reservoir, the navigation of permanent shiplock and shiplift, and the power production of the first sets of generating units. Phase-three of the project construction will be from 2004-2009 and the following major works will be completed: the installation of all other generating units and the finish of the whole project.

After the completion of the project, it will benefit in flood control, power generation, navigation, tourism, ecology projection, environmental purification, develop-oriented resettlement, water transmission from south to north and irrigation. These are ten advantages that no hydro plant in the world can possess.

ird's-Eye View of the Dam

■ The Great Yangtze Three Gorges Project

Great Events in Three Gorges Project Construction

1. Mr. Sun Yat-Sen, the forerunner of China Democratic Revolution, firstly conceive the notion of improving the navigation channel of Yangtze River in Sichuan and utilizing the upstream river to produce power in Strategy for State, Part II: Industrial Plans in 1919.

2. In October 1932, the Resource Committee of Kuomintang organized a reconnaissance and conducted a two-month field survey and measure in the Three Gorges area for the first time, and then formed The Report on the reconnaissance of the Hydropower in Yangtze River.

3. In May 1944, the famous dam expert, the general engineer in Bureau of Reclamation in United States Dr. Sovage was invited to China to visit the Three Gorges in the midst of Japanese enemy's gunfire. He then wrote famous "The Preliminary Report on the Project of Yangtze Three Gorges", which is the first detailed plan in regard to the comprehensive utilization of Hydropower in Yangtze Three Gorges.

4. The People's Republic of China was founded in October 1949, and the Yangtze River Water Conservancy Committee was established in Wuhan in February 1950.

5. In July 1956, Chairman Mao wrote a famous poem: Walls of stones will stand upstream to the west/To hold back Wushan's clouds and rain/Till a smooth lake rises in the narrow gorges/The mountain goddess if she is still there/Will marvel at a world so changed. It is a poem that describes the splendid blueprint of the Three Gorges Project for the first time.

6. On March 1, 1958, Premier Zhou Enlai, accompanied by relevant ministries of State Council, Representatives of the cities and provinces along the Yangtze River and experts of China and the Soviet Union, totally more than 100 people, visited Nanjingguan and Sandouping, the potential damsites of the TGP. Premier Zhou clearly pointed out that Sandouping was a preferable damsite, and his statement is an important decision about damsite.

7. On March 30, 1958, Chairman Mao visited the Yangtze Three Gorges on a riverboat before attending the Chinese Communist Party Central Committee Meeting in Chengdu.

8. On April 25, 1958, the CPC Central Committee Meeting passed "The CCPCC Statement of the Three Gorges Hydro Plant and the Arrangement of Yangtze Basin", the first document issued by CCPCC concerning Three Gorges Project.

9. On December, 26, 1970. The Central Committee of CPC and the State Council permited the construction of Gezhouba Hydro Plant as an essential part of Yangtze Three Gorges Key Water Control Projects, and pointed that it was preparation for the construction of TGP. Gezhouba project started power generation in 1981 and totally completed in 1989.

10. The Feasible Report of Three Gorges Project was submitted to the State Council in February 1984, which confirmed a tentative plan of building a 150-meter Dam. It also decided the establishment of the Preparation Team of TGP, the Preparatory Group of Sanxia Province and Three Gorges Project Development Corporation.

11. At the end of 1984, Chongqing Municipal Committee of CPC reported Some Opinions on the Yangtze Three Gorges Project to the CPC Central Committee and officially opposed the 150-meter Dam Plan and advanced a plan of 180-meter Dam. There were some members of Chinese People's Political Consultative Conference and communities opposing the former plan.

12. In June 1986, Circular of CPC Central Committee and State Council Concerning the Justification of Yangtze Three Gorges Project was issued, charging Ministry of Water Conservancy and Electric Power to organize the specialists from various aspects and collect their suggestions, in order to further justify and revise the original feasible report on TGP. Hence, a new feasible report was made and the Preparatory Group of Sanxia Province was dismissed. According to the decision of CPC Central Committee, 14 specialist groups, submitted

to Ministry of Water Conservancy and Electric Power, were charged to conduct a three-year of justification review activities.

13. On March 6 1992, Premier Li Peng handed The Proposal of the State Council Concerning the Review of the Application of the Construction of the Three Gorges Project to the Fifth Session of the Seventh National People's Congress. On the 3rd of April, 2633 representatives of the National People's Congress voted on the proposal with 1767 pros, 177 cons, 466 abstention and 25 not pressing the button. The proposal was approved, and justification review was replaced by construction. What Chinese people dreamed of in the last century was going to be realized.

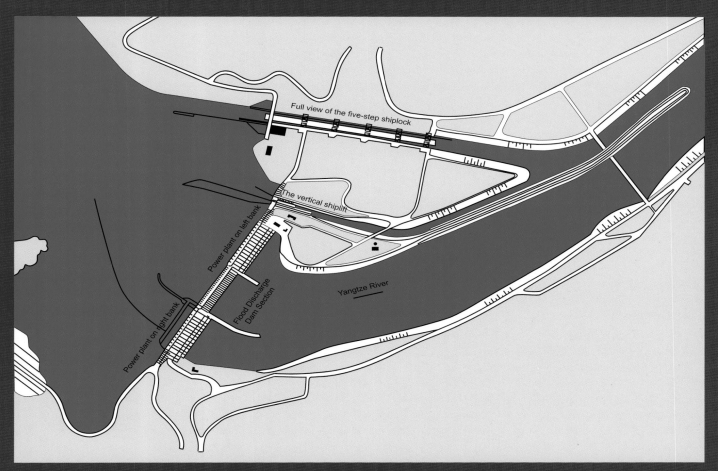

Sketch Map of the Three Gorges Project

The Three Gorges Dam Site

A crucial and fundamental factor of the water conservancy project is ensured by the dam site as well as high water level, and some related specific technical problems of the project such as the scale, efficiency, and difficulty etc are also determined by them.

The dam site is located in Zhongbaodao Island of Sandouping Town in Yichang county, Hubei province. In the 1950's, Sandouping Town was first chosen by the government from fifteen dam sites of the two dam areas. Then, in view of the project protection and development by stages, Shibei Town and Taipingxi Town was once considered in the 1960's. Finally, Zhongbaodao Island of Sandouping Town was selected as the dam site in the 1980's. In total, the choice lasted for more than 20 years.

Sandouping Island is an ideal foundation for high-dam construction for it is waterproof with solid and complete granite as the bedrock. In addition, the valley of the Island is easy to widen and convenient to construct as it is comparatively wide with low hills on both sides. Furthermore, Zhongbaodao Island has provided the favorable topographical and geological conditions for diversion construction by stages since it can be used to build longitudinal cofferdam and thus can divide Yangtze River into two sections: 900-meter-wide and 300-meter-wide respectively. As is mentioned above, Zhongbaodao Island is a gift from nature to the Chinese nation.

Rock Core Drilled at Dam Site

三峡工程
CHINA
中国 Three Gorges Project

Construction Schedule

According to the procedure, the construction of TGP is composed of three phases and lasts 17 years. Since the hydropower project should be built on land rather than in water, the river closure is quite necessary. After the closure, the foundation pit will impound water, so that the surface weathered granite layer can be removed and the dam can be built on the interior rocks. It means that during the construction, the Yangtze River must change its course. That is why there should be channel change and close-off. The Zhongbaodao Island which is located in the middle of the river divides the river into the main channel and the diversion channel, providing favorable land condition for the channel change. The plan adopted is: first degree exploiture, one-off completion, water storage by stages and continuous resettlement.

Phase I

1993-1997 phases I channel change

Use the phase-I cofferdam to build the diversion channel. The river and all the ships pass through the main channel. The river closure succeeded in November 1997, which indicates the completion of phase I construction target.

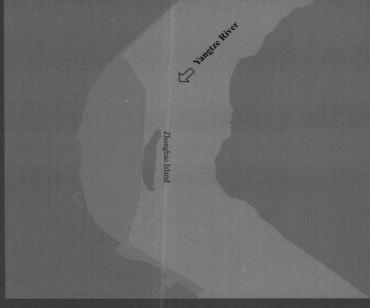

Original Look of the Three Gorges Site

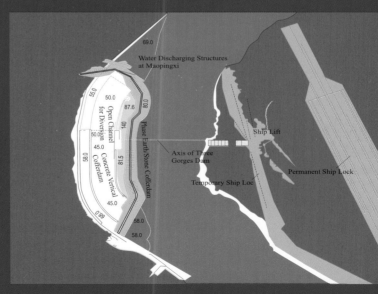

Map of the 1st Stage Construction

Phase II

1998-2003 phase II channel change
The major works are: the phases-2 cofferdams, construction of the spillway dam, left bank dam section and left bank powerhouse. The river spills from the diversion channel, and ships pass through the diversion channel or the temporary shiplock. The success of the close-off of the diversion marks the completion of the second phase.

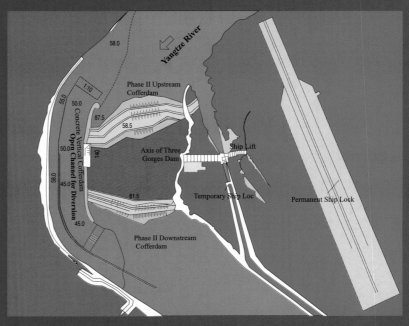

Map of the 2nd Stage Construction

Phase III

2004-2009 phase III channel change
Closure of the diversion channel and the concrete cutoff wall will be finished, which will form the phase-III foundation pit. The dam construction on the right bank and the installation of all other generating units will be completed. At that time, the Yangtze River will pass the spillway dam from 23 bottom outlets, 22 surface sluice gates and outlets, and all the ships go through the permanent double-way and five-step shiplock. The construction will be realized by the power generation of all the units and the completion of the whole structure.

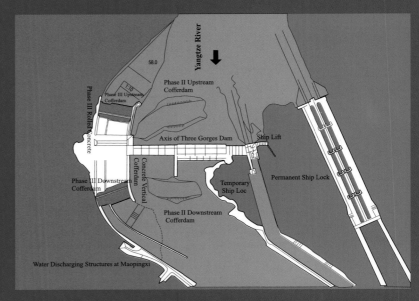

Map of the 3rd Stage Construction

▢ The Great Yangtze Three Gorges Project

三峡工程
CHINA
中国 Three Gorges Project **The Plan of Three Gorges Project**

Right Bank Construction Site

The Great Yangtze Three Gorges Project

Panoramic View of Phase III Construction Site

The Great Yangtze Three Gorges Project

Night Scene during the 3rd Stage Construction

The Great Yangtze Three Gorges Project

Diversion and closure

Construction diversion scheme by stages (thrice cofferdam construction, closure twice, diversion in three stages, and navigation of open diversion channel and temporary shiplock construction) has been adopted by experts and constructors in Three Gorges Project after many years of research.

The main task of the first step is to build concrete longitudinal cofferdam with Zhongbaodao Island as the foundation so as to prevent water from utilizing earth rock cofferdam. Open diversion channel is excavated according to navigation and diversion. Meanwhile, the foundation of the concrete cofferdam in the third phase should be completed. During this period, navigation and flood discharge are still fulfilled on the main stem. The second step is to carry out closure for the first time on the main stem by upstreamcofferdam and downstreamcofferdam and form the second phase foundation pit on the main stem and the left bank so that phase II project will be under construction in the following. Making use of open diversion channels for navigation together with diversion and the left bank temporary shiplock help to reduce the construction period in this phase. The third step is to implement the second closure in open diversion channels and then form the third phase foundation pit by roller compaction concrete cofferdam built in dry season. In this way, the third phase project can be accomplished after the second one. The temporary shiplock is of no use and a measure called "transportation across the Dam" which lasts about half a year is introduced to transport people and luggages by land before the beginning period storage of the Three Gorges reservoir reaches 135 meters and after the second closure is completed. Furthermore, diversion bottom channel set in closure dam is made use of during this period. After the reservoir reaches 135 meters, the three gorges project permanent shiplock of the fifth level was in use on June 16th,2003. All those practices prove that this scheme is of great success.

River Closure of the Yangtze River (February,1997)

River Closure of The Open Diversion Channel (February, 2002)

The Successful River Closure of The Open Diversion Channel (February, 2002)

■ The Great Yangtze Three Gorges Project

三峡工程

CHINA

Three Gorges Project

The Plan of Three Gorges Project

Open DiversionChannel in Navigating

The Transportation

The traffic of the project

During the construction of the Three Gorges project, large quantities of materials and equipment especially many heavy equipment and large scale equipment need importing. After the experts' long time study and identification, an efficient and economical scheme of taking the highway (the highway between Yichang city and the dam site, its' eastern part joining Han Guang Highway) as main and concurrent with water transport has finally been adopted. Consequently, the scheme proves to be correct.

Xiling Yangtze Bridge

Expressway Special for Three Gorges Project

The Liantuo Bridge

Spillway Dam

The spillway dam, one section of the Three Gorges Dam, is located in the middle of the river course. With the length of 483 meters, the spillway dam connects the two powerhouses at both sides. The dam is equipped with 23 bottom outlets, 22 surface sluice gates and outlets with other functions. The dimensions of the bottom outlets are 7m-9m, while the net width of the surface sluice gates is 8m. The Maximum discharge capacity of the dam is 102,500 m^3/s.

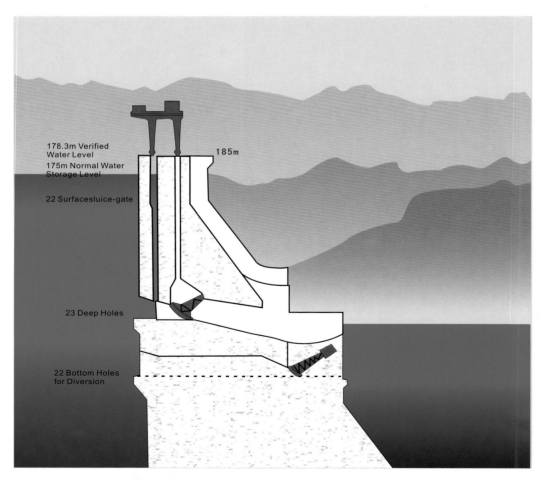

The Sketch of the Spillway Dam Cross Section

Spillway Dam Cross Section

■The Great Yangtze Three Gorges Project

三峡工程

Spillway Dam

Spillway Dam Cross Section

The Great Yangtze Three Gorges Project

Navigation Structures

The permanent navigation structures consist of the permanent double-way and five-step shiplock and a shiplift, both of which are located in the mountain area on the left bank. The overall length of the permanent shiplock is 6442 m, with the length of the main body 1607 m, upper lock approach 2113 m and lower lock approach 2722 m. Each lock chamber is dimensioned at 280 m $\times$ 34 m $\times$ 5 m (length $\times$ width $\times$ min. depth), capable of passing 10,000-t barge fleet. The annual single-way passing volume of the shiplock is 50 million tons.

The shiplock is deeply excavated and constructed in sound granite mountain masses on the left bank, and it is entitled the Forth Gorge of the Yangtze River. Subject to excavation and relief of stress in rock body, a lot of unstable wedge-shaped rock blocks are existed during the construction. In order to strengthen the bedrock and ensure a good stability of the side slopes, 3,600 pre-stressed tendons, with a capacity of 300 tons each, and another 100,000 high-strength structural rock bolts have been installed on the side slopes. On June 15, 2003, the double-way and five-step shiplock is navigated successfully.

The double-lane five-stepshoplock service

Virgin Navigation

Virgin Navigation

■ The Great Yangtze Three Gorges Project

三峡工程

Temporary Shiplocks

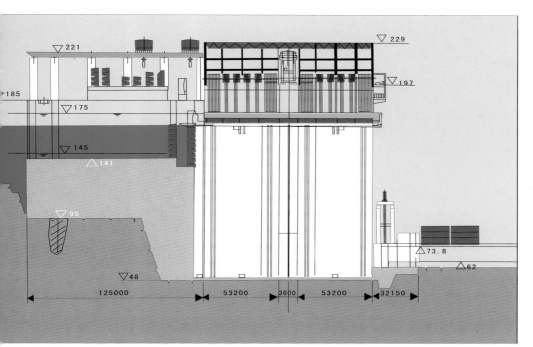

Shiplift

The shiplift is schemed as a single-way and one-step vertical hoisting type with a ship container sized 120m×18m×3.5m, capable of carrying one 3,000 ton passenger in 45 minutes.

What distinguish the Three Gorges Dam and other dams in the world are the large-scale shiplock and shiplift, which can be compared to an elevator. Although waiting for an elevator need time, vertical movement can quickly deliver people to their destiny.

A Sketch Map of the Shiplift

Powerhouses of TGP

Two powerhouses are placed at the toe of the dam. There are 26 sets of hydro turbine generator units installed in total, 12 on the right bank and 14 on the left. With 700 MW for each unit, it ranks the biggest hydro turbine generating system in the world. In July 2003, the first group of units began to generate power.

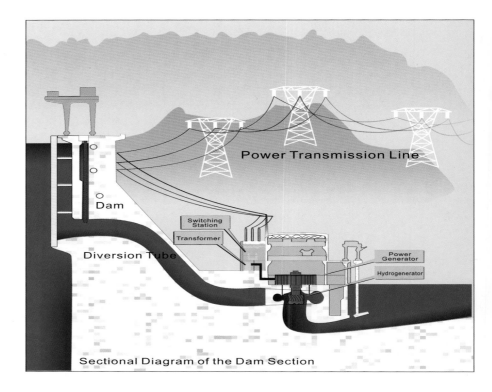

Sectional Diagram of the Dam Section

1. The Sketch of the Powerhouse Cross Section
2. Internal view of the Powerhouse
3. Night Scene of the Powerhouse

■ The Great Yangtze Three Gorges Project

三峡工程

Snail's Shell Technics

Ø12.4m Penstock

■ The Great Yangtze Three Gorges Project

三峡工程

Rotor(1,694.5 Tons) Installation

The Rotor of the World's Largest Hydro Turbine

The Great Yangtze Three Gorges Project

三峡工程

CHINA

Three Gorges Project

Powerhouses of TGP

The underneath Powerplant

The underneath Powerplant

The underneath Powerplant

Water Export

■ The Great Yangtze Three Gorges Project

三峡工程
CHINA
中国 Three Gorges Project

World Records Set by TGP

1.The most effective project in flood control
The overall storage capacity of TGP is 3.93 billion m^3, and its flood control capacity 22.15 m^3, which can effectively control the flood from upstream river and strengthen the ability of flood control in middle and down stream.

2.The biggest hydroelectric plant
TGP's rated capacity is 18,200 megawatt, and the average annual power generation if 84.68 billion KWh.

3.Construction of the largest scale
The total length of the dam axis is 2,309.47 m, and the spillway dam is 484 m long. There are 26 sets of hydro turbine generator units in total, 300 MW for each. The major structure also includes a double-way and five-step shiplock and a shiplift. The TGP boasts concrete placement of 27.94 million m^3, rock-and-earth excavation and refill of 134 million m^3 and metal frame installation of 463 thousand tons.

4.The highest intensity of concrete placement
World records for concrete placement were set during sequent three years. In 2000, the annual concrete placement was 5.4817 million m^3 and monthly concrete placement was 550 thousand m^3.

5.The channel change with the strictest requirements
The largest discharge estimated during the closure is 10,000m^3/s. The cofferdam in deep water is 60m high.

6.The spillway dam with the largest discharge capacity
The maximum discharge capacity is 102,500m^3/s.

7.The inland shiplock with the most steps and the highest total water head
The Three Gorges shiplock is a double-way and five-step shiplock with the total water head of 113 m.

8.The shiplift of the largest scale and toughest work
The Three Gorges shiplift has the effective water area of 120 m×18 m×3.5 m. The maximum lifting height is 113 m. The average tonnage of ship is 3,000 tons and the total lifting weight is 11800 tons.

The Subsidiary Dam the Non-overflow Dam at Maoping Xi Brook

The Great Yangtze Three Gorges Project

Comparison of the World's 8 Greatest Hydropower Stations

Country	Hydropower Stations	River	Total installed capacity (MW)	Power generation/year (TWh)
China	Three Gorges	Yangtze River	18200	84.68
Brazil and Paraguay	Itaipu	Parana River	12600	71
USA	Grand Coulee	Colunbia River	10830	20.3 (in the initial stage)
Venezuela	Guri	Caroni River	10300	51
Brazil	Tucurui	Tocantins River	8000	32.4 (in the initial stage)
Canada	La Grande Stage II	La Grande River	7326	35.8
Russia	Sayano-Shushensk	Yenesei River	6400	23.7
Russia	Krasnoyarsk	Yenesei River	6000	20.4

List of Main Features of the Project

Item Description		Unit	Index	Note
Reservoir	Normal Pool Level	m	175	156m in the intial stage
	Flood Control Level	m	145	135m in the intial stage
	Design Flood Level	m	175	
	Check Flood Level	m	180.4	
	Total Storage Capacity	Billion m³	39.3	
	Flood Control Capacity	Billion m³	22.15	
	Surface Area	km²	1,084	
Dam	Type		Concrete gravity	
	Crest Elevation	m	185	
	Max.Height	m	181	
	Length of the Axis	m	2,039.47	
Power Station	Length of Left Powerhouse	m	643.7	
	Number of Units in Left Powerhouse	Set	14	
	Length of Right Powerhouse	m	584.2	
	Number of Units in Right Bank	Set	12	
	Capacity per Unit	MW	700	
	Total Installed Capacity (Excluding Underground Powerhouse)	MW	18,200	
	Annual Electricity Output (Excluding Underground Powerhouse)	Twh	84.68	
	Number of Units in Underground powerhouse	Set	6	
	Installed Capacity in Underground powerhouse	MW	4,200	
Ship Lock	Type			Double way,5 stage
	Size of Chamber	m	280×34×5	
Ship Lift	Type			One way,5 stage
	Size of Chamber	m	120×18×3.5	

■ The Great Yangtze Three Gorges Project

Flood Control

Precipitation in Yangtze Basin has the characteristic of monsoon climate, and the discharge from June to September take 70-75% of the total annual one. According to historical records, 214 heavy floods occurred during the 2096 years between 1911 AD and 185 BC, approximately once in every 10 years. Since 1911, 11 severe floods have occurred in the Yangtze basin, once per 6 years. The Yangtze River, one of the Mother Rivers of the Chinese nationality, brings countless disasters to people who live along it. Ancient legends about harnessing river and other historical documents display the nation's bittersweet history of 5000 years.

In 1870, an unusually great flood struck 16 km^2 and people were plunged into an abyss of misery. In 1931, about 145,000 people were killed in the flood. In 1935, the number is 142,000. 33,000 people died the flood in 1954, and 1526 died in another flood in 1998.

Flood control is one of the major objects of building TGP. The designed flood control standard is 1000-year recurrence and the actual standard is 10% more than that. It is the most effective project in flood control all over the world. TGP's maximum discharge ability of river channel is 120,600m^3/s. Compared with the annual discharge of 960 billion m^3 of the Yangtze River, the flood control capacity of TGP (22.15 m^3) is not very large. However, the project can regulate the flood by slowing down the speed of flood peak and storing water. It can help cut flood peak by 30% after it passes through the dam, so that the discharge to the middle and down stream can be effectively lessened. Nowadays, TGP is the key project in the flood control system of middle and down stream of the Yangtze River, protecting 15 million people, 2.3 million hectares of farmland and cities in the Jianghan Plain and Dongting Lake from flood threats and devastating plagues.

Flood Spill

Flood Spill

Social and Economy Benefits of
Three Gorges Project

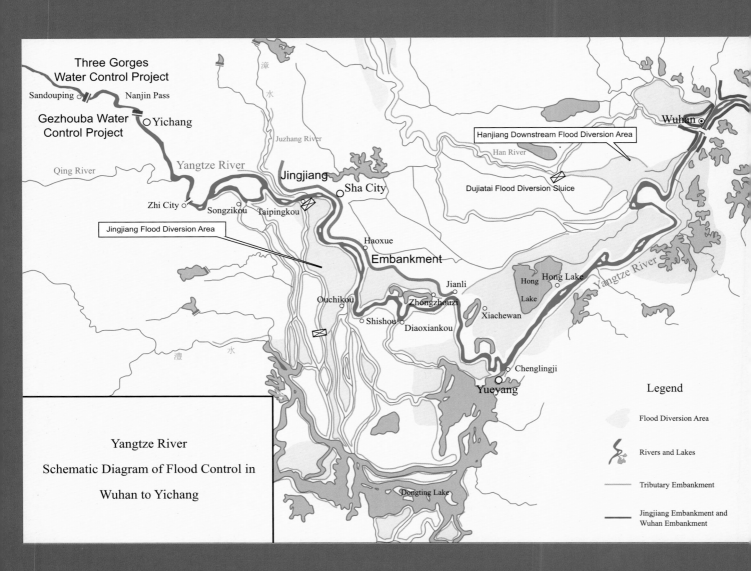

三峡工程
CHINA
中国 Three Gorges Project   **Flood Control**

**Three Gorges
Water Control Project**
Sandouping ○   Nanjin Pass

**Gezhouba Water
Control Project**   ○ Yichang

Qing River   Yangtze River

漳
水

Juzhang River

Jingjiang   ○ Sha City

Zhi City ○   Songzikou
Taipingkou

Hanjiang Downstream Flood Diversion Area

Han River

Wuhan ○

Dujiatai Flood Diversion Sluice

Jingjiang Flood Diversion Area

Haoxue

Embankment

Jianli

Hong   Hong Lake

Lake

Yangtze River

Ouchikou   Zhongzhouzi

Shishou   Diaoxiankou   Xiachewan

澧
水

Chenglingji

Yueyang

Legend

Flood Diversion Area

Rivers and Lakes

Dongting Lake

Tributary Embankment

Yangtze River

Schematic Diagram of Flood Control in

Wuhan to Yichang

Jingjiang Embankment and
Wuhan Embankment

Jingjiang Levee

三峡工程
CHINA
Three Gorges Project

Power Generation

The roaring Yangtze River is rich in hydropower resources, and the Three Gorges Project is the biggest hydropower plant in the world. The project consists of two powerhouses, which are respectively located at the toe of the dam. There are 26 sets of hydro turbine generator unit installed in total, 12 on the right bank and 14 on the left. With 700 MW for each unit, the overall installed capacity is 182,000 MW and the average annual power generation is 86.68 billion KWh. The power generation capacity of TGP equals to five times of the capacity of Gezhouba Hydropower Plant or ten times of that of Dayawan Nuclear Power Station. TGP has broken the world records in both unit capacity and overall installed capacity.

In order to fully exert TGP's advantage in power generation, another 6 sets of hydro turbine generator unit are installed in the underground station in the right bank mountain. With 700 MW for each unit, the overall capacity of the underground station is 42,000 MW, which equals to 1.5 times of the capacity of Gezhouba Hydropower Plant. Since the infalls of the underground station and the whole project will be completed synchronously, the actual TGP generator unit is added to 32 sets and the overall capacity will reach 224,000 MW.

The position of the Three Gorges Project is favorable because the power supply radius is about 1000 km, covering more than 50% of Chinese territory. At present, the Three Gorges Power is transmitted to Middle China, East Sichuan Province, South China by 500 kV HVAC lines, and to East China by -500 kV HVDC lines. The Three Gorges Power System will provide credible, cheap and clear reproducible electricity for the east, middle and south China, where energy is not enough to support the rapid economic development.

The Control Center of the Three Gorges' Powerhouse

The first tower of the Three Gorges

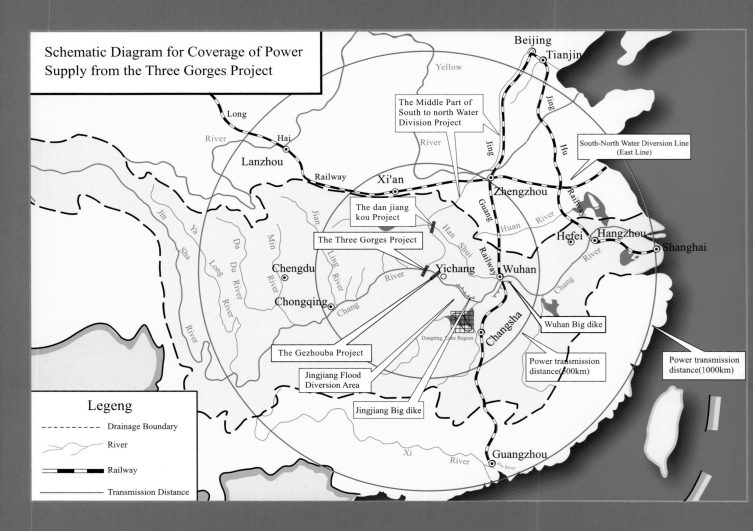

三峡工程
CHINA
中国 Three Gorges Project   Power Generation

Schematic Diagram for Coverage of Power
Supply from the Three Gorges Project

Beijing
Tianjin

The Middle Part of
South to north Water
Division Project

South-North Water Diversion Line
(East Line)

Yellow

Long

Hai

Railway

Lanzhou

Xi'an

Zhengzhou

Jing

Hu

Railway

The dan jiang
kou Project

The Three Gorges Project

Guang

Huan

River

Hefei

Hangzhou

Shanghai

Jin

Ya

Sha

Da

Du

River

Min

River

Jian

Ling River

Han Shui

Railway

Chengdu

Chang

River

Yichang

Wuhan

Chang

River

Chongqing

Long

River

The Gezhouba Project

Dongting Lake Region

Changsha

Wuhan Big dike

Jingjiang Flood
Diversion Area

Power transmission
distance(500km)

Power transmission
distance(1000km)

Jingjiang Big dike

Legeng

- - - - - - Drainage Boundary

River

Railway

Transmission Distance

Xi

River

Guangzhou

Zhu River

Longquan Convertor Station

CHINA
中国 Three Gorges Project

Navigation

The Yangtze River is entitled "Golden Watercourse" in history. However, in the past, there were many dangerous invisible shoals which made the water flow rapidly from Sichuan Province to Yichang in Hubei Province. There is an old saying that: The way to Sichuan is very tough, even tougher than going to the heaven. Therefore, the history of navigation in the Yangtze River in Sichuan and west Hubei Province is full of miseries and hardships. After the establishment of the People's Republic of China, though the explosion of the reefs and the harness of the channel were never stopped, the river course was still not smooth enough. Some reaches were so narrow that only small ships within 1000-t can pass. During dry season, Jingjiang course in the middle stream of the Yangtze River can also be navigated by small ships within 1000 tonnage.

When the construction of TGP is completed, the navigation in the Yangtze River will be remarkably promoted and hereafter that, the river in Sichuan Province will be no longer dangerous and become the real "Golden Watercourse". At that time, the 660-km route from Yichang to Chongqing will be improved, which can largely enable 10000-tonnage fleets to navigate directly from Shanghai, the east city, to Chongqing. The annual one-way navigation capacity of the Yangtze at the dam will be upgraded from ten million tons to fifty million tons. Moreover, the ship terminals are greatly enhanced. The load capacity per watt will increase 2.72-5.44 tons, while the oil consumption is 1/30 of the former one. Furthermore, since the river flow velocity decreases and navigation during night becomes safer, time consumed for each voyage will be shortened and the cost will be reduced by 35-37%. The situation that the watercourse in middle and down stream is not smooth enough especially in dry season will be changed. Therefore, the navigation in the Yangtze River is stepping forward to a new stage, which will greatly facilitate the economic development in west China.

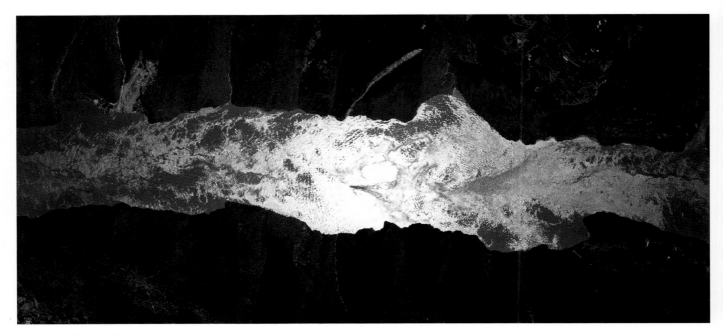

Yangtze Golden Waterway

The New Three Gorges River-route

三峡工程

CHINA ▪

Three Gorges Project

Navigation

Lantern

Trace Marks

The Plank Road

The Three Gorges Tracker

One Million Migrants

The resettlement is a world-class barrier during the construction of TGP, and it will have a key effect on the success or failure of the project construction. TGP is a world famous huge project, while the arrangement of such a large scaled resettlement and the submerged area is the first time in the history of the water conservancy and hydropower project construction of mankind in the world. When the Three Gorges Reservoir is impounded up to the normal pool level at EL 175 m above sea level, the total inundated land involves 21 counties, cities or district in Hubei Province and Chongqing Municipal City, including cultivated land, citrus land and forest of 420,000 mu (28,000 ha). Approximately 1.13 million people are estimated to be relocated. Calculated on the basis of price level of May 1993, 40 billion as static fund is allocated to the resettlement program.

The principle adopted for the construction is that: first degree exploiture, one-off completion, water storage by stages and continuous resettlement. Hence, governments at all levels have taken the opportunities to resettle the migrants. By the end of 2002, about 689.4 thousand people were accommodated in the reservoir region with fund used to upgrade their living standards. Another 100 thousand people moved out of the reservoir region and relocated in 25 provinces, cities and autonomous areas of the country. A series of policies framed to "Development-oriented Resettlement" were issued and implemented, so as to make steady economic foundation for the emigration, accommodation and enrichment of Three Gorges migrants. It is because of those ordinary Chinese people committing to their obligations that the resettlement and the construction of TGP can proceed successfully.

The Imitation street of Han Dynasty in Zi Gui

New County Seat of Wushan

三峡工程

CHINA

Three Gorges Project

One Million Migrants

Resettlement of Residents for Three Gorges Project

New County Seat of Zigui

Resettlement Town

三峡工程
CHINA
中国 Three Gorges Project

Sedimentation

Whether the construction of TGP will trigger sedimentation is a controversial problem attracting people from every aspect of the society. The designers of TGP spare no efforts to solve this problem. The following three goals concerning sedimentation should be achieved: 1. the reservoir cannot be full of silt; 2. partial sedimentation cannot affect navigation; 3. the method of "storing clear water in dry season and flushing muddy water in flood season" will not cause regradation in down stream.

In order to prevent the silt up of reservoir, measures to control sedimentation must be adopted in reservoir operation and project construction. Hence, favorable geographical conditions should be well utilized. The Three Gorges Reservoir is a river-like one. The 600 km-long reservoir has the average width of less than 1000 m, with only a small area 1000-1700 m wide. It has a narrow and deep section with few shoals. According to the theoretic analysis and silt mode tests home and abroad, since the

sediments are carried into the reservoir by the inflow mainly during flood season, the method of "storing clear water in dry season and flushing muddy water in flood season" can effectively maintain the reservoir capacity for quite a long term. The detailed measures are: during flood season from June to September when the river contains a large portion of silt, the reservoir water level will be lowered to limit EL. 145 m, and the river discharge and silt will pass the deep sluices, which is called "flushing muddy water in flood season". After the flood season, there is less silt entering the reservoir, and the water level will be raised to EL. 175 m, which is called "storing clear water in dry season". During the process, there are sediments depositing in the reservoir but not affecting its effectiveness of operation. When the water level is lowered to the lowest level in the next flood season, the river discharge can flush most of sediments away, leaving a little silt depositing near the shoals. As time passes by, part of sediments will be retained in downstream water till the reservoir

Reservoir Deposition

reach silt-deposit-sluice equilibrium. In this way, the Three Gorges Reservoir can preserve normal operation permanently without being destroyed by sedimentation.

The ultimate ways to reduce sedimentation are to afforest in the upstream mountains along the Yangtze River, to continue water and soil conservation project and to construct large-scale reservoirs on the branches so as to prevent silt running to the main channel.

Sands Cleanup

Blocked Sediment

三峡工程
CHINA
中国 Three Gorges Project

Ecological Environment Protection

The world-class project brings world-class challenge. Considering sustainable development of the environment, scientists have conducted objective analysis and careful arrangement on the environment, resettlement and fund, etc., so as to cover every problem involved reasonably and scientifically, and to make sure that in two or three decades after the completion of TGP, the Three Gorges Reservoir Area will become a beautiful place benefiting soil conservation and the ecology.

After the impoundment of the reservoir, the Three Gorges Dam began to control flood from the year 2003. In June 2003, the double-way and five-step shiplock started to work. In the next month, the first sets of generator unit start to produce power. TGP's advantage in profits gaining as well as environment protection begins to show itself. The project will play an important role in improving the ecology along the Yangtze River and in promoting the sustainable development of the society and economy.

The construction of TGP will benefit sustainable development of ecological environment along the Yangtze River. The researches on its influence on environment started early in the 1950s, and the result shows that TGP is of great meaning in improving ecological environment.

TGP will provide with a large amount of clear electricity. Compared with coal power plant producing the same amount of electricity, which will consume 40-50 million tons of raw coal and release 100 million tons of carbon dioxide, 2 million tons of sulfur dioxide, 10 thousand tons of carbon monoxide, 370 thousand tons of oxynitride and a great deal of dust and waste residue, TGP can effective reduce the negative influence brought by glasshouse effect and acid rain, and meliorate the environment in middle and east China.

The key point in ecological environment protection is to maintain water quality in reservoir area and in down stream as well. Since the water pollution in some sections of reservoir is getting serious, when constructing TGP, a number of sewage works are built at the same time to dispose polluted water. Meanwhile, the Three Gorges Reservoir can stabilize the inflow in down stream, so that swage disposal can be conducted conveniently. Therefore, the Yangtze water quality in dry season can be great improved, and so is the water quality in Shanghai City. Moreover, since TGP can control flood, the environmental deterioration and the spread of infectious disease triggered by flood and flood diversion can be avoided. The Three Gorges Reservoir can also ameliorate the regional climate in reservoir area, providing favorable conditions for the development of agriculture, forestry, fishing and other industries. Motivated by the construction of TGP, all kinds of industry prosper, infusing vitality and energy for the economy in Three Gorges area, which is now becoming a place more suitable for the living of humanity.

The impoundment of reservoir offers enormous water resources for the Project of Diverting Water from the Yangtze River to North China.

Harmonious Reservoir Area

Earthquake

The damsite is located at Sandouping, Yichang City, on the ancient crystal rocks in pre-sinian epoch. The bedrock of riverbed is granite, covered with thin layers. The weathered rock on both banks is about 20-30 m thick, while on riverbed it is very thin and the bedrock is sound, with homogeneous lithology and large mechanical strength. The rocks have extremely low permeability and small faults in high deep angle. In the area of 10 km around the damsite which is covered with crystal rocks, there are no active faults and other prominent negative geophysical phenomenon.

TGP is located on a relatively stable block, Huangling Block, which will lead to strong earthquake. It is an area where earthquake occurs with low intensity and frequency. The reservoir-induced earthquake is a kind of advance energy release induced by the impoundment of reservoir, and a natural earthquake usually happens in a glance. There is little possibility that two kinds of earthquakes occur simultaneously. Taking every negative factor into consideration, scientists conclude that the severest earthquake will not exceed 7 on the Richter scale, the critical scale that can be withstood by the dam.

Foundation Laying on the Left Bank

遵章守法 铸造精品

Foundation of the Dam

■ Solution of Momentous Problems of Three Gorges Project

■ Solution of Momentous Problems of
Three Gorges Project

Potential Menace of War

The Three Gorges Power Plant is not only the energy resources for east, middle and southwest china, but also important transportation artery between east and west. It is certainly a major striking target during wartime. Therefore, threats of war are considered when TGP is constructed.

TGP is situated in the very middle of China. As a concrete gravity dam, the Three Gorges Dam is capable of defending conventional weapons because of its immensity and advantageous location. Facing the threats of nuclear weapons, the dam is possible to collapse, which is the worst situation. Except for the necessary protective measures used during construction, other methods, for instance, lowering the reservoir water level, will be adopted. Since every war can be pre-warned, discharging the water beforehand can reduce the harm brought by the collapse of dam. Furthermore, experts point out that the 30 km-long zigzag section between damsite and the nearest downstream city can slow down the speed of flood in case the dam is destroyed. When the flood passes through Nanjinguan and enters foothill, the water will flow more quietly and slowly so that the flood can be mitigated. In extremely emergent occasion, the reservoir water level can be lowered further, and the power plant will become a run off one. As a result, the damage of collapse will be eliminated.

China is a peace-loving nation with strong sense of responsibility. Holding the policy of "Peaceful development", China will avoid any potential war by trying to unit all the forces that can be united to maintain a peaceful world. Meanwhile, it is universally acknowledged that China is a country with nuclear weapons, possessing a variety of anti-aircraft tactic missiles as well as strategic missiles with different striking ranges. It can not only intercept enemy missiles but also conduct second-strike to enemies at any place in case of war.

Sunglow

Sources of Fund

TGP is a large-scale and long-term project with fund from diverse sources, including the state investment, mortgage from the State Development Bank of China and domestic commercial banks, issuing corporate bond, capital raised by equity participation, export credit, and foreign exchange loan from banks abroad.

1. Capital

The Three Gorges Fund

Benefits yielded by Gezhouba Power Plant

Refund of income tax and dividend distribution of China Yangtze Power Co., Ltd

Benefits yielded by TGP and refund of income tax

Fund from the above four sources is 80 billion Yuan, taking up 45% of the Total Project Investment, 180 billion Yuan. The Three Gorges Fund comes from state capital, which is one of the most stable fund sources.

2. Policy-related loan

As a policy-based bank, the State Development Bank of China began to provide loan at the commencement of construction in 1994. From 1994 to 2003, SDBC provided loan of 3 billion Yuan annually, 30 billion in total, and it plays an active role in the start-up of construction. Policy-related loan from SDBC is one of the most stable fund sources.

3. Corporate bond

Issuing corporate bond is a way to raise fund with little cost directly from capital market. By the end of 2003, 6 terms of Three Gorges bond were issued with a total amount of 19 billion Yuan.

4. Equity participation

China Yangtze Power Co., Ltd was listed in 2003 and became an approach for equity participation in capital market, which has enlarged the channel of capital collecting.

By the end of 2003, fund from loans of domestic commercial banks, export credit, and foreign exchange loan from banks abroad is 11 billion Yuan.

Item	Unit	Parameters
Total static investment	RMB Billion yuan	90. 09
Hydraulis structures	RMB Billion yuan	50. 09
Compensation due to reservoir inundation	RMB Billion yuan	40
Total dynamic investment	RMB Billion yuan	203. 9
Estimated total investment	RMB Billion yuan	180

Project Economy and Finance Analysis

In the phase of justification review and preliminary scheme, there is a comprehensive analysis on the project economy and the feasibility and rationality of finance, in respect of future profit gaining. The result is that constructing TGP will bring profits and can be invested. The Preliminary Sketch Report of Three Gorges Project (December, 1992) indicates that the financial internal rate of return is 11.5%, term of mortgage is 24.59 years, and the pay back period of investment is 19.2 years.

In 2003, the initial impoundment of reservoir, the navigation of permanent shiplock and the power generation of the first group of units mark the completion of the first two constructive periods. According to the consumption of fund, the total project investment can be limited within 180 billion Yuan, and the future economic efficacy of the project is better than that estimated in feasibility research and preliminary report.

The Airscap of the Project

■ Solution of Momentous Problems of Three Gorges Project

CHINA
三峡工程
中国 Three Gorges Project

Gezhouba Hydropower Plant

Gezhouba, first Hydropower Plant on the Changjiang River, is a large-scale power station designed and constructed independently by Chinese people. As an indispensable component of Three Gorges Project, Gezhouba Hydropower Plant can regulate the tail water fluid state of TGP and improved the steps of shipping conditions between two dams. Situated in the urban area of Yichang City, the entrance of Yangtze Three Gorges, it is 2.3 kilometers away from Nanjinguan of the Xiling Gorge and 38 kilometers away from the Three Gorges Dam of the upper reaches.

The Yangtze River rushes out of Nanjinguan and opens up from 300 m to 2200 m suddenly. The river is divided into three strands by two narrow islands, Gezhouba and Xiba. The project gains the name from the name of the damsite, Gezhouba.

The Gezhouba Dam is 2606.5 m long and 70 m high. The whole project covers an area of about 9 sq. km., consisting of a block dam, three shiplocks, two hydropower houses, a release sluice gate, two scouring sluice and a water-blocking wall. There are 27 outlets on the release sluice gate, with discharge capacity of 110,000 m^3 per second. 21 sets of generator unit are installed in total, and the overall installed capacity is 2,715,000 KW, with annual generation of 15,700 million KWh. The electricity generated by Gezhouba is transmitted to Shanghai, Henan, Hunan, Wuhan and other places. Among three single-step shiplocks in Gezhouba, two can navigate 10,000-t ships. The annual one-way navigation capacity is more than 50 million tons.

The construction of Gezhouba Hydropower Plant began on December 30, 1970, and completed in an all-round way on December 20, 1998. In May 1982, the reservoir started to impound water. The total investment for construction of the project is 4,800 million Yuan. The Gezhouba Dam has withstood two 100-year floods happened in 1981 and 1998, and is still safe and sound.

A Airscape of the Gezhou Ba Dam

List of Principle Indices of the Gezhouba Project

Item Description	Unit	Index
Drainage Area	Km^2	100×10^4
Designed Pool Level	m	66
Crest Elevation	m	70
Total Storage Capacity	m^3	15.8×10^8
Annual Average Runoff	m^3/s	14,300
Designed Flood Runoff(Flood in 1788)	m^3/s	86,000
Check Flood Runoff(Flood in 1870)	m^3/s	110,000
Handled Ship Tonnage of No.2	t	$(1.2\text{-}1.6)\times10^4$
Handled Ship Tonnage of No.3	t	0.3×10^4
Total Installed output Capacity	kw	271.5×10^4
Annual Average Power Generation	Kwh	160×10^8
Max.Flood Sluice of 27 Outlets	m^3/s	86,900
Length of the Axis	m	2,606.5
Concrete Placement	m	1.113×10^4
Earth & rock Excavation and Embankment	m	1.113×10^8
Mental Works	t	7.75×10^4

■ Gezhouba Hydropower Plant

Three Gorges' culture and historic site protection

The protection of historic relics in the dam site such as ancient buildings, towns and stone inscriptions etc have attracted people's attention both at home and abroad after the Three Gorges' reservoir storage. For example, these inundated or negatively affected historic relics such as Baihe Liang in Fuling, Zhangfei Temple, Shibao Zhai and Qu Yuan Shrine etc are protected according to a measure that is protecting at the original place and rebuilding when moved to another site, and besides, these inundated precious ancient tombs are digged out and cleaned after a careful survey.

Shibao Zhai Village of Zhongxian County

After the conservation storage of the Three Gorges Project, the protection work of historic sites such as the ancient buildings, ancient towns and stone engravings of the reservoir area of Three Gorges have been concerned greatly by Chinese and foreigners. The historic site that floods, influences, for instance Baihe Liang, Zhang Fei Temple, Shibao Zhai Village, Qu Yuan Shrine,etc. are protected under the principle of "Protect in the original site and rebuild in a new site", the underground ancient tombs in the flooding area have been carried on exploration on the basis of general survey too.

The Shibao Zhai Village lay within the boundaries of Zhong County of Chongqing at the north bank of the Yangtze River. This village was established in the Wanli year of Ming Dynasty that has already had a history of more than 300 years so far. The tower building is 12 stories that is 56 meters high. It was built on the huge stone of a fatherless peak. Because the stone looks like a jade and people said it used to be a colored stone that it was left over form Nukua according to legend it is also called "Yuyin Shan (Jade Seal Mountain)". Tanhong a revoltor in late Ming Dynasty, considered here as his base the "Shibao Zhai (stone treasure village)" was name from this. The village is a pearl in art of ancient architecture of our country, it boasts one of the "Eight world's Wonders" and also a "AAAA" scenic spot of China.

After the normal pool level of the Three Gorges Project reaches 175 meters, Shibao Zhai and the Yuyin Shan Mountain will be affected due to the geographical change. Thus a new plan of "Bank Protection by Adding Steel Gate" raised by Yangtze River Survey Planning and Design Institute in 2002 will be adopted to prevent the Yuyin Shan Mountain from deformation, and effectively dispose the underground water will be another important issue of the relic protection project. Anyway, the whole program is going to spend more than 100 million Yuan.

After the Three Gorges Project is completed, when visitors pass by the Shibao Zhai Village they will see the only detached island in the reservoir area of Three Gorges. It is asking the village to become the world largest "potted landscape", standing in the Yangtze River where the mist-covered waters ripples.

■ Three Gorges' culture and historic site protection

Zhangfei Temple

Zhang Fei (god of butchers) Temple lies the South bank of the Feifeng Shan Mountain of Yunyang County in Chongqing. It was built for Zhang Fei, star of Shu Han of the Three Kingdom Period. Zhang Fei Temple is made up of a group of old architectures, its main buildings include 7 different pavilions such as Zheng Dian, Pang Dian, Jieyi Lou, Wangyun Xuan, Zhufeng Ge, Dujuan Ting and Deyue Lou etc. The former 5 buildings were built for commemorating Zhang Fei and the later 2 were for commemorating a great poet Du Fu who once lived there for two years in the Tang Dynasty. It is a rare temple with both military and arts.

In July of 2003, Zhang Fei Temple has already been moved to the Yangtze River bank more than ten kilometers on the upper reaches. The whole resettlement project exactly followed the original one that it had not merely saved a brick and one watt from the original temple but the site selection is similar to the original temple location also. In this case the exhibition area was increased and the whole impact had been better.

1.Zhufeng Ge
2.Zhangfei Temple in Yunyang
3.Inside of Zhangfei Temple

Zhangfei Temple
(before relocation)

Zhangfei Temple
(after relocation)

■ Three Gorges' culture and historic site protection

Baidi Cheng Town

Baidi Cheng Town lies on the top of Baidi Mountain, which is on the north bank of the west end of the Qutang Gorge. The delicate buildings and verdant plants have ever attracted lots of visitors. The great poet Li Bai of Tang Dynasty had wrote " Baidi I left at dawn; in the morning-glow of the clouds; the thousand li to Jiangling; we sailed in a single day. On either shore the gibbons' chatter; sounded without pause; While my light boat skimmed past; a thousand somber crags." Due to this poem the Baidi Cheng became a famous one and a resort of the Three Gorges.

According to the historical records: Gong Sunshu occupied the Shu state and proclaimed himself the king in late Xi Han Dynasty. Once he built a city on a mountain, and discovered a well in the city emitted white air, like a white dragon. Then he called himself "Baidi (the White King)" and so the city Baidicheng was named after this. After his death, locals built the Baidi temple

There are Mingliang Dian, Wuhou Shrine and Guanxing (view star) Pavilion that were built in Ming and Qing Dynasties in the Baidi Temple. On both sides of the temple there are 74 stone tablets established in the past dynasties another large-scale painted sculpture in the front hall of the temple, present the story of "Liu Bei entrusts his young son to the minister". One who has read Romance of the Three Kingdoms, "knows the story" Liu Bei entrusts his young son to the minister, and this is the place where the story happened. In A.D. 222, Liu Bei lead 200,000 main forces the east lay, revenge for Guan Yu who is Liu's senior general but he was end up beaten in Jianping of Wushan, before his death he entrusts his three sons to the prime minister Zhu Ge-liang. Place oneself in this Baidicheng Town, it seems that it is in the history of the Yangtze River.

There is not a bit influence on Baidi Cheng with the water level rise to 139 meters in the reservoir of the Three Gorges Project. At present Baidi Cheng is surrounded by water on three sides, the other side connects to mountain. Baidi Cheng, where has been an important historical site 2000 years ago, today had already turned into a beautiful peninsula where there will build a beautiful shelter bridge connect it to the north bank of the Yangtze.

1.Sculptures
2.City Gate to Baidi Cheng
3.Baidi Cheng with Bird's Eye View

3

Qu Yuan Shrine

Qu Yuan Shrine is located at the old city of Guizhou Town, which covers only 0.6 square kilometers. The Guizhou Town has the history of over 2300 years. It has experienced different historical periods such as Warring States period, the Three Kingdoms period, Tang, Song, Ming as well as the Qing Dynasties. The town is considered as an unsubstituted witness of changes of the Yangtze Three Gorges.

Qu Yuan, (c. 340 BC - 278 BC) also called Ping. He was born in Leping Li of old Zigui County and was a Chinese patriotic poet from southern Chu during the Warring States Period. Qu Yuan was a minister in the government of the state of Chu, descended a champion of political loyalty and truth eager to maintain the Chu state's sovereignty. The Chu king, however, fell under the influence of other corrupt, jealous ministers who slandered Qu Yuan, and banished his most loyal counselor. In his exile, he spent much of this time producing some of the greatest poets such as "Li Sao", "Jiu Zhang" and "Jiu Ge" while expressing his fervent love for his state. Eventually, he suisided and his death is commemorated on Duan Wu Festival, commonly known as the Dragon Boat Festival. In the year 1953, Qu Yuan was ranked the World Cultural Celebrity by the UNESCO.

The present Qu Yuan Shrine was moved and rebuilt in 1976 due to the construction of the Ge Zhou Ba project. The pool lever of the Three Gorges Project reached 139 meters hasn't impacted the shrine a lot, anyway with the Three Gorges Project holding water once again, as a "relocated project" it faces the second relocation. It will be moved to the east and rebuilt on the Fenghuang Shan Mountain of Zigui County.

Qu Yuan Shrine

Three Gorges' culture and historic site protection

Da Chang Ancient Town

Da Chang Ancient Town of Wushan County is the biggest town along the Daning He River of the Yangtze Three Gorges. The east- west main street is 450 meters long and the north-south street is less than 300 meters long. There are three well preserved city gates in the east, west and south respectively. The architectures of Dachang are exquisite and unique and most of them were built in Qing Dynasty, which was more than 1700 years ago.

Gratifiedly, although the Three Gorges Project holds water once again in 2006, this beautiful ancient town was "cloned" in a new place several kilometers away from the original one. The Da Chang Ancient Town will become a Da Chang lake, stories and legends of this 1700 years old ancient town will become people's eternal memory.

1.The East Gate of the Ancient Town
2.The Southen Gate of the Ancient Town
3.A Corner of Ancient Town
4.Grotesque Cypresses in the Ancient Town

The Xin Tan Ancient Residences

The Xin Tan ancient local-style residences lie in west section of Xiling Gorge, the other bank of Gui Lin village of Qu Yuan town (original Xin Tan town), Zigui county. It is the largest ancient residence in the whole Three Gorges area, with the most remote history, and vivid characteristics.

Here were only 3 towns that completely kept the beautiful natural living environment of mountains and rivers in Three Gorges area before 2002. These are: Da Chang, Ning Chang and Gui Lin village of Xin Tan ancient towns. And among them Gui Lin village stands in the breach when we talk about the classical intensity, artistic level and natural scenes of the three towns.

The special characteristics of Gui Lin Village are "crooked means". The gates of the residences are all a bit inclined, and the laneways appear angled. It is due to the ancient theory of "feng shui expert" the local omen is too prosperous, only by using this unusual way of "crooked means" would keep the favorable "feng shui" for good. The only ones that can compare with Gui Lin village is the ancient town of Xin Tan on the other bank in Three Gorges area. Unfortunately, this town was destroyed by an enormous landslide in the middle of 1980s which made the village of Gui Lin outshine the others. However, with the reservoir of the Three Gorges Projects, today the Gui Lin village is all gone, but it's main building has already been rebuilt on the Fenghuang Shan Mountain.

∎ Three Gorges' culture and historic site protection

Reconstruction of Ancient Architectures

Fenghuang Shan scenic spot of Zigui County is a site for rebuilding the ancient architectures. There is a Qu Yuan park, which is under construction to memorize Qu Yuan and show the civilization of the Yangtze Three Gorges. Its main part includes Qu Yuan Shrine, Tianwen Tai, museum and Chu Feng Lou etc. Rebuild 24 Yangtze Three Gorges local-style residences and historical relic here, that people and nature, history and reality getting along with each other. While visitors are wandering around here and looking at the Three Gorges Dam from afar, it just likes entering the spatio-temporal tunnel. On every Dragon Boat Festival, under the Fenghuang Shan Mountain local people are still in this kind of unique way of dragon boat regatta to commemorate the world famous cultural talent Qu Yuan.

After "the high gorge rise from the flat lake" the Fenghuang Shan mountain became starting point of the new Three Gorges, the mountain itself has been turned into a beautiful peninsula. The Fenghuang Shan Mountain is only one kilometer away from the Three Gorges Dam and its favorable geographical position always makes visitors passionate.

Duplicate Jiangdu Temple

Hydrological Stone Inscription of the Three Gorges Reservoir Area

There are a lot of hydrological stone inscription s along the Yangtze River, but most of them have been engraved during the flood season, fewer were in the dry season. Among them the most precious one Baihe Liang lies in the middle of the Yangtze River in the north of the Fuling city of Chongqing Municipality. This stone engraving has a very important value of scientific research and historical reference. The stone is about 1600 meters long and 16 meters wide, it is covered with different engravings enclose "the stone fish predicts a bumper harvest year", explaining the law of good years.

After the completion of the Three Gorges Projects, Baihe Liang will be flooded throughout the year. Through repeatedly demonstration Baihe Liang's hydrological stone Inscription protection project finally used the "no pressure container" to protect the original piece under water. In the dense area of Inscriptions a special structure will be built and the water pressure on the two sides of this structure get balance due to the water supply from a filter device. A sealed corridor in the structure will joint the ground, by this means visitors can see the engravings at a short range through the special anti-pressure window.

After the subaqueous museum finish the construction a subtil and huge protective shell will be there like a submarine to attract lots of visitors.

With the Three Gorges project began to save water some of the other famous stone Inscriptions like "dragon beds stone" known as Longchuang Shi in Fengdu County and "dragon back stone" known as Longji Shi in Yunyang County have already sunk to the bottom of the Yangtze forever.

1

2

3

4

1.Dragon Spine Stone
2.Dragon Bed Stone
3.Stone Fish
4.Baihe Liang in Fuling

The Three Gorges Stone Inscription

There are several types of stone engravings in the Three Gorges area such as epigraphy, cliff inscription and natural stone engraving. Most of them were engraved on the cliff or reefs. And the contents are records of floods, low water and river way dredging projects, some of them are boundary restriction items, however there are more engravings about passion and emotion toward the great mountains and river.

Before the Three Gorges Project started to raise water in its reservoir, some of the precious stone engravings were protected. The most famous cliff inscription in Qu Tang Gorge was reconstructed according to the principle of "former address protection", by this means the unique heritage could be extended generation by generation.

1 . "Gap between Hubei and Sichuan"
   Natural Stone Carving
2 .Precipice Stone Carving at Sanyou Cave
3 .Inscription at Qu Tang Gorge after Reconstruction

Precipice Stone Carving at Qu Tang Gorge after Reconstruction

■ Tourism of New Three Gorges

Tourism of New Three Gorges

The Yangtze Three Gorges is the most magnificent, beautiful and mysterious section of the Yangtze River. It is one of the top 10 sceneries in China. Beginning from Baidi Cheng in Fengjie County of Chongqing in the west and extends to Nanjin Guan in Yichang of Hubei province in the east. Three sections as the Qutang Gorge, the Wu Gorge and the Xiling Gorge consist the great "Yangtze Three Gorges" within 200 kilometers waterway.

The huge project also brought people worries: will the Three Gorges still beautiful? Compared with the natural water level, the water in the Three Gorge reservoir will be 70-100 meters higher and the width of the water surface will be 100 meters wider than it used to be. In this case people might think the feeling of the high gorge would be not as that great as before. Actually, the mountains on both sides of the river are about one hundred meters high, and some of the peaks are even higher than 1000 or 2000 meters above the sea level. For example, the peaks in the Qutang Gorge are more than 1000 meters high, even if the water level rise when the TGP finish, the 40 meters increased height just reaches the bottom of the peaks. The Shennv Feng (known as the Goddess Peak) is 900 meters high, and 50 meters water level rise would do a very little affect to its view, just as Chairman Mao once described in his poet: "walls of stones will stand upstream to the west to hold back Wushan's clouds and rain till a smooth lake rises in the narrow gorges. The mountain goddess if she is still there will marvel at a world so changed".

After the water level change in the Three Gorges reservoir lots of the scenery along the upstream of the dam have been changed. The Mini Three Gorges although is not as before, the other sights along the tributary of Daning He River became more beautiful especially the Tiny Little Three Gorges. The Shennong Xi Brook and Xiangxi He River that share a same headstream with the Daning He River, after the water level rise, visitors can experience the adventurous water rafting and even enter and discover the mysterious Shennong Jia from the Three Gorges by waterway.

With the construction of the Three Gorges a huge and long "lake" substitutes the old Yangtze watercourse, the scenic area has been greatly enlarged since there are more scenic spots came into being in the tributary of the Yangtze. Some of the interesting places such as the world's wonder the Heavenly Pit, the Earthly Ditch and Gaolan scenic area could be only reached by road in the past now visitors can easily get there by boat.

The Three Gorges Project has effectively protected the tourism resources of the Three Gorges area, and it has brought fresh air into the development of the Three Gorges tourism which gets rebirth from the great social and economic benefits.

三峡工程

Goddess Peak

Mysterious Wushan Mountain

三峡工程

CHINA

Three Gorges Project

Sightseeing of Yangtze Three Gorges

Spring in the Three Gorge

Tourism of New Three Gorges

三峡工程

CHINA

Three Gorges Project

Sightseeing of Yangtze Three Gorges

Summer in the
Three Gorge

三峡工程

Autumn in the Three Gorge

Autumn in the Three Gorge

Winter in the Three Gorge

三峡工程

CHINA ■

Three Gorges Project

Sightseeing of Yangtze Three Gorges

三峡工程

Ghost City(Fengdu of Chongqing)

The Three Gorges Dam Area

Qu Tang Gorge/Baidi Town Scenic Spot (Fengjie Chongqing)

The Lesser Three Gorges of Daning He River(Wushan of Chongqing)

三峡工程

CHINA ▪

Three Gorges Project

The Three Gorges Dam Area

Drifting Scenic Spot at Shennongxi Brook (Badong Hubei)

三峡工程

CHINA

Three Gorges Project

The Three Gorges Dam Area

The Three Gorges Dam Area(Yichang of Hubei)

Dachang Town •

The Lesser Three
Gorges on the
Daling River ▲

Shengiongxi River ▲

New Fengjie County •   New Wushan County

▲ Baidi Town

Bianyu Stream ▲

▲ Goddess peak

• Daxi Town

• Qingshi

Qutang Gorge

▲ Shennu Stream

Wuxia Gorge

Tourist Sketch Map of the Three Gorges

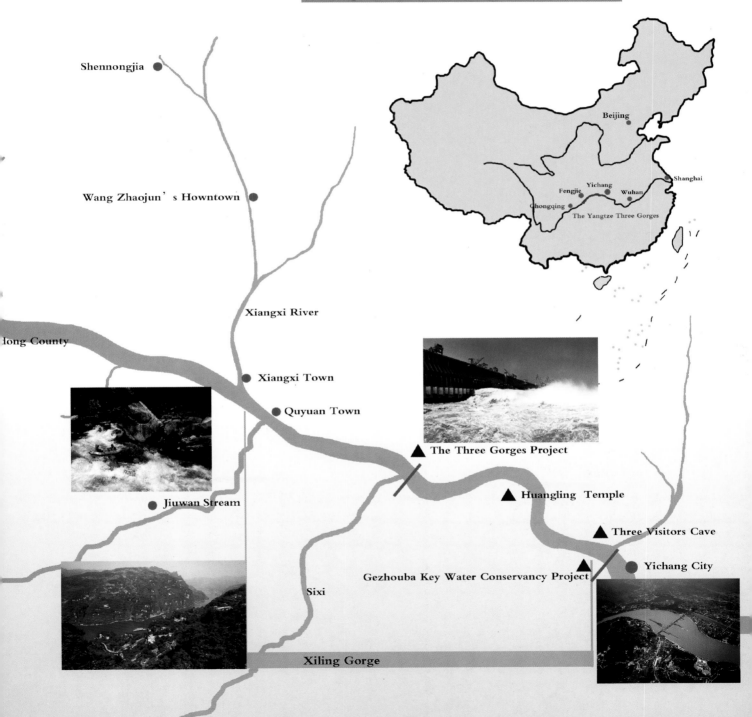

Geographical Position Map of the Yangtze Three Gorges in China

Shennongjia

Wang Zhaojun's Howntown

Xiangxi River

Xiangxi Town

Quyuan Town

dong County

Jiuwan Stream

The Three Gorges Project

Huangling Temple

Three Visitors Cave

Gezhouba Key Water Conservancy Project

Yichang City

Sixi

Xiling Gorge

Beijing

Shanghai

Fengjie   Yichang

Chongqing   Wuhan

The Yangtze Three Gorges

國書在版編目（CIP）數據

中国三峡工程/卢进主编
—北京：中国方正出版社，2009.3
（长江三峡风光画册精品系列）
ISBN 978-7-80216-473-4
Ⅰ．中... Ⅱ．卢... Ⅲ．三峡工程—画册Ⅳ.TV632.71-64
中国版本图书馆CIP数据核字（2009）第020664号

长江三峡风光画册精品系列

中国三峡工程（英文版）

主　　編：盧　進

責任編輯：陶　瑩
裝幀設計：朱紅霞　　　　　　　　翻　譯：江　天
攝　　影：盧　進　黄正平

　　　　　楊榮輝　王連生

　　　　　閆　偉
出版發行：中國方正出版社
　　　　　（北京市西城區平安裏西大街41號　郵編：100813）
　　　　　發行部：（010）66560938　讀者服務部：（010）66562755
　　　　　編輯部：（010）59596606　出版部：（010）66510958
　　　　　網　址：www.fzpress.com.cn
　　　　　責編E-mail：Fangzheng1313@126.com
經　　銷：新華書店
制作印刷：深圳市精典印務有限公司
開　　本：20開
印　　張：6.4
版　　次：2009年3月第1版 2010年5月第2次印刷
書　　號：ISBN 978-7-80216-473-4
定　　價：138元